GRID AND BEAR IT

Graphing Activities for Listening and Following Directions
Grades 1–3

Will C. Howell

Fearon Teacher Aids • Carthage, Illinois

ISBN 0-8224-3510-1

Contents

Introduction

The activities in *Grid and Bear It* are designed to develop listening skills, provide practice in following directions, reinforce left/right awareness, and provide readiness for coordinate geometry and graphing. Whether listening or reading, students will follow directions and move their pencils to create clever pictures that are fun to make. Before you begin, a bit of organizing information will be helpful.

Contents
Grid and Bear It has thirty-three reproducible activities. The first twenty-one activities are designed for one-inch grid paper. The last twelve activities are designed for one-half-inch grid and one-half-inch coordinate grid paper. Reproducible blackline masters of the three types of paper are located in the back of the book.

Directions
Directions for the activities are presented in two distinct formats: descriptive directions and coordinate directions. For descriptive directions, a starting point is located, and then students are directed to move along the lines of the grid paper. For example: "Move your pencil left 3 spaces, down 2 spaces, right 1 space, up 4 spaces . . ."

Coordinate directions focus on a grid point to start and then direct the student to move from one grid point to another. For example: "Start at A-2. Move your pencil to B-2, B-5, C-5 . . ." Coordinate directions are provided on separate reproducible activity sheets. All activity directions may be read aloud to students or duplicated and distributed for students to complete independently.

Answer Key
For each activity a reduced image of the final product is provided on the same page as the descriptive directions. This reduced image can be used as the answer key for the activity. The images are the same for the final products of both descriptive and coordinate directions.

Preparation
Select an activity and duplicate the appropriate grid paper. If you plan to distribute the activity sheets with the descriptive directions, simply cover the answer-key image with a blank piece of paper before duplicating. Students will need a sheet of grid paper, a pencil, and an eraser. They will need an activity sheet if they are to be working independently.

Using Descriptive Directions

Activity directions indicate whether the paper is to be placed horizontally or vertically.

horizontally

vertically

Next, students are directed to find the starting point by locating a beginning horizontal or vertical line and then counting a given number of spaces in a specific direction. Students should move along a line of the grid paper as they count the given number of *full* spaces. Full spaces are blocks that have all four corners visible. (Grid paper duplicated from the back of this book will not present a problem in locating the starting point or counting full spaces; however, commercial graph paper may have edges with spaces that are not complete. If you use commercially printed graph paper, be sure your students understand the concept of *full* spaces.)

Moving the Pencil

Students construct the picture by drawing a continuous line from the starting point; their pencils should not be lifted from their papers. A teaching suggestion for younger students: you might have them mark the left (L) and right (R) edges of their papers to help them avoid reversals.

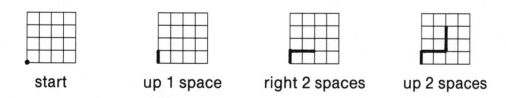

start   up 1 space   right 2 spaces   up 2 spaces

Using Coordinate Directions

For the one-half-inch coordinate directions, students will locate the starting points by finding a letter across the bottom and a number along the left edge of the paper. For example: A–1

Students should find the letter line and the number line and follow each line until the two intersect. The intersection of the horizontal and vertical lines is the starting point. Students locate each point in sequence and move their pencils continuously.

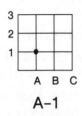

A–1

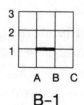

B–1

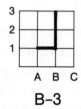

B–3

Completing the Picture
After completing all the steps of an activity, students are directed to add details to their drawings, such as ears, eyes, and nose.

Geoffrey Giraffe

Paper: one-inch grid

Starting point:

1. Place your paper vertically.
2. Find the left end of the horizontal line closest to the upper left corner of your paper.
3. Count one full space to the right.
4. Move down one full space.
5. Make a pencil dot on the intersection of the horizontal and vertical lines.
6. Put your pencil on the dot.

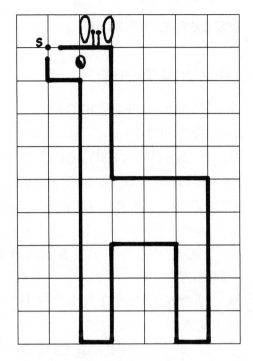

Move your pencil:

1. Right 2 spaces
2. Down 4 spaces
3. Right 3 spaces
4. Down 5 spaces
5. Left 1 space
6. Up 3 spaces
7. Left 2 spaces
8. Down 3 spaces
9. Left 1 space
10. Up 8 spaces
11. Left 1 space
12. Up 1 space

Add: ears, eye, horns

Perky Pickup

Paper: one-inch grid

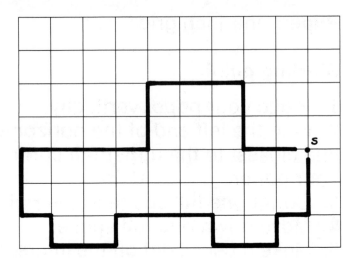

Starting point:

1. Place your paper horizontally.
2. Find the right end of the horizontal line closest to the upper right corner of your paper.
3. Count one full space to the left.
4. Move down four full spaces.
5. Make a pencil dot on the intersection of the horizontal and vertical lines.
6. Put your pencil on the dot.

Move your pencil:

1. Down 2 spaces
2. Left 1 space
3. Down 1 space
4. Left 2 spaces
5. Up 1 space
6. Left 3 spaces
7. Down 1 space
8. Left 2 spaces
9. Up 1 space
10. Left 1 space
11. Up 2 spaces
12. Right 4 spaces
13. Up 2 spaces
14. Right 3 spaces
15. Down 2 spaces
16. Right 2 spaces

Scotty Dog

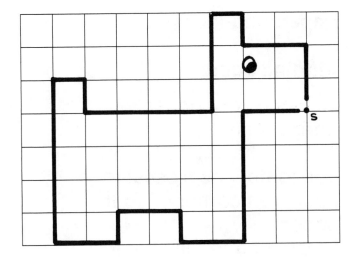

Paper: one-inch grid

Starting point:

1. Place your paper horizontally.
2. Find the right end of the horizontal line closest to the upper right corner of your paper.
3. Count one full space to the left.
4. Move down three full spaces.
5. Make a pencil dot on the intersection of the horizontal and vertical lines.
6. Put your pencil on the dot.

Move your pencil:

1. Up 2 spaces
2. Left 2 spaces
3. Up 1 space
4. Left 1 space
5. Down 3 spaces
6. Left 4 spaces
7. Up 1 space
8. Left 1 space
9. Down 5 spaces
10. Right 2 spaces
11. Up 1 space
12. Right 2 spaces
13. Down 1 space
14. Right 2 spaces
15. Up 4 spaces
16. Right 2 spaces

Add: eye

Calvin Camel

Paper: one-inch grid

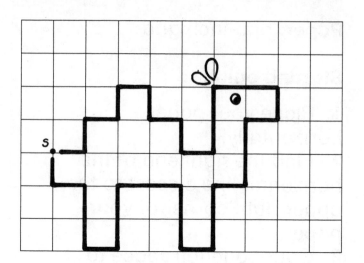

Starting point:

1. Place your paper horizontally.
2. Find the left end of the horizontal line closest to the upper left corner of your paper.
3. Count one full space to the right.
4. Move down four full spaces.
5. Make a pencil dot on the intersection of the horizontal and vertical lines.
6. Put your pencil on the dot.

Move your pencil:

1. Right 1 space	13. Left 1 space
2. Up 1 space	14. Down 2 spaces
3. Right 1 space	15. Left 1 space
4. Up 1 space	16. Down 2 spaces
5. Right 1 space	17. Left 1 space
6. Down 1 space	18. Up 2 spaces
7. Right 1 space	19. Left 2 spaces
8. Down 1 space	20. Down 2 spaces
9. Right 1 space	21. Left 1 space
10. Up 2 spaces	22. Up 2 spaces
11. Right 2 spaces	23. Left 1 space
12. Down 1 space	24. Up 1 space

Add: ears, eye

Kangaroo for You

Paper: one-inch grid

Starting point:

1. Place your paper vertically.
2. Find the top of the vertical line closest to the upper left corner of your paper.
3. Count down five full spaces.
4. Make a pencil dot on the intersection of the horizontal and vertical lines.
5. Put your pencil on the dot.

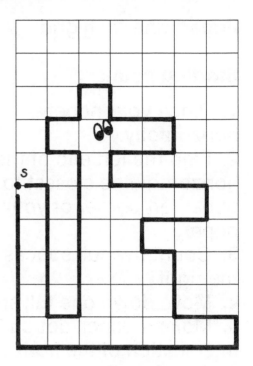

Move your pencil:

1. Right 1 space
2. Down 4 spaces
3. Right 1 space
4. Up 5 spaces
5. Left 1 space
6. Up 1 space
7. Right 1 space
8. Up 1 space
9. Right 1 space
10. Down 1 space
11. Right 2 spaces
12. Down 1 space
13. Left 2 spaces
14. Down 1 space
15. Right 3 spaces
16. Down 1 space
17. Left 2 spaces
18. Down 1 space
19. Right 1 space
20. Down 2 spaces
21. Right 2 spaces
22. Down 1 space
23. Left 7 spaces
24. Up 5 spaces

Add: eyes

Picture a Pagoda

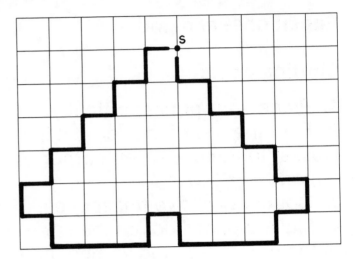

Paper: one-inch grid

Starting point:

1. Place your paper horizontally.
2. Find the left end of the horizontal line closest to the upper left corner of your paper.
3. Count five full spaces to the right.
4. Move down one full space.
5. Make a pencil dot on the intersection of the horizontal and vertical lines.
6. Put your pencil on the dot.

Move your pencil:

1. Down 1 space
2. Right 1 space
3. Down 1 space
4. Right 1 space
5. Down 1 space
6. Right 1 space
7. Down 1 space
8. Right 1 space
9. Down 1 space
10. Left 1 space
11. Down 1 space
12. Left 3 spaces
13. Up 1 space
14. Left 1 space
15. Down 1 space
16. Left 3 spaces
17. Up 1 space
18. Left 1 space
19. Up 1 space
20. Right 1 space
21. Up 1 space
22. Right 1 space
23. Up 1 space
24. Right 1 space
25. Up 1 space
26. Right 1 space
27. Up 1 space
28. Right 1 space

Grid and Bear It ©1987

Chugging Choochoo

Paper: one-inch grid

Starting point:

1. Place your paper horizontally.
2. Find the top of the vertical line closest to the upper right corner of your paper.
3. Count down three full spaces.
4. Make a pencil dot on the intersection of the horizontal and vertical lines.
5. Put your pencil on the dot.

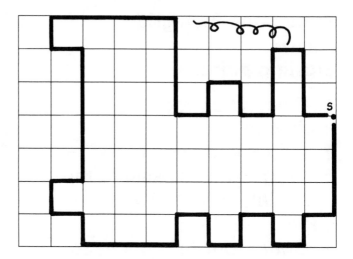

Move your pencil:

1. Down 3 spaces
2. Left 1 space
3. Down 1 space
4. Left 1 space
5. Up 1 space
6. Left 1 space
7. Down 1 space
8. Left 1 space
9. Up 1 space
10. Left 1 space
11. Down 1 space
12. Left 3 spaces
13. Up 1 space
14. Left 1 space
15. Up 1 space
16. Right 1 space
17. Up 4 spaces
18. Left 1 space
19. Up 1 space
20. Right 4 spaces
21. Down 3 spaces
22. Right 1 space
23. Up 1 space
24. Right 1 space
25. Down 1 space
26. Right 1 space
27. Up 2 spaces
28. Right 1 space
29. Down 2 spaces
30. Right 1 space

Add: smoke

Eager Elephant

Paper: one-inch grid

Starting point:

1. Place your paper horizontally.
2. Find the left end of the horizontal line closest to the upper left corner of your paper.
3. Count four full spaces to the right.
4. Move down one full space.
5. Make a pencil dot on the intersection of the horizontal and vertical lines.
6. Put your pencil on the dot.

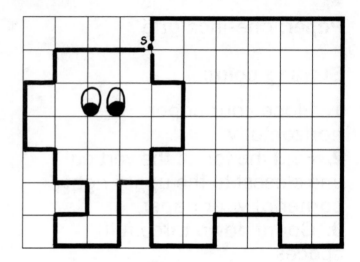

Move your pencil:

1. Up 1 space	10. Right 1 space	19. Down 1 space
2. Right 6 spaces	11. Up 2 spaces	20. Right 1 space
3. Down 7 spaces	12. Left 1 space	21. Down 1 space
4. Left 2 spaces	13. Up 1 space	22. Left 1 space
5. Up 1 space	14. Left 3 spaces	23. Down 1 space
6. Left 2 spaces	15. Down 1 space	24. Right 2 spaces
7. Down 1 space	16. Left 1 space	25. Up 2 spaces
8. Left 2 spaces	17. Down 2 spaces	26. Right 1 space
9. Up 3 spaces	18. Right 1 space	

Add: eyes

Peekaboo Mouse

Paper: one-inch grid

Starting point:

1. Place your paper horizontally.
2. Find the left end of the horizontal line closest to the lower left corner of your paper.
3. Count five full spaces to the right.
4. Move up one full space.
5. Make a pencil dot on the intersection of the horizontal and vertical lines.
6. Put your pencil on the dot.

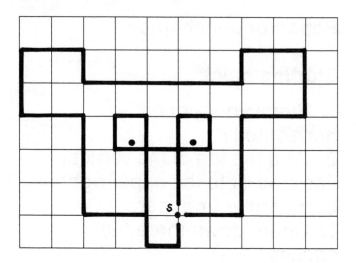

Move your pencil:

1. Down 1 space
2. Left 1 space
3. Up 1 space
4. Left 2 spaces
5. Up 3 spaces
6. Left 2 spaces
7. Up 2 spaces
8. Right 2 spaces
9. Down 1 space
10. Right 5 spaces
11. Up 1 space
12. Right 2 spaces
13. Down 2 spaces
14. Left 2 spaces
15. Down 3 spaces
16. Left 2 spaces
17. Up 3 spaces
18. Right 1 space
19. Down 1 space
20. Left 3 spaces
21. Up 1 space
22. Right 1 space
23. Down 3 spaces

Add: eyes

Don't Pet a Panther

Paper: one-inch grid

Starting point:

1. Place your paper horizontally.
2. Find the top of the vertical line closest to the upper right corner of your paper.
3. Count down three full spaces.
4. Make a pencil dot on the intersection of the horizontal and vertical lines.
5. Put your pencil on the dot.

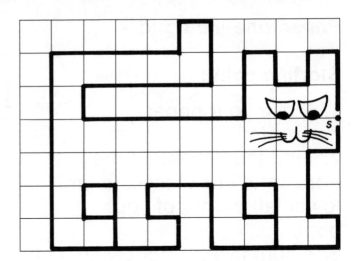

Move your pencil:

1. Up 2 spaces
2. Left 1 space
3. Down 1 space
4. Left 1 space
5. Up 1 space
6. Left 1 space
7. Down 2 spaces
8. Left 5 spaces
9. Up 1 space
10. Right 4 spaces
11. Up 2 spaces
12. Left 1 space
13. Down 1 space
14. Left 4 spaces

15. Down 6 spaces
16. Right 2 spaces
17. Up 1 space
18. Left 1 space
19. Up 1 space
20. Right 1 space
21. Down 2 spaces (return over your line)
22. Right 2 spaces
23. Up 1 space
24. Left 1 space
25. Up 1 space
26. Right 2 spaces
27. Down 2 spaces

28. Right 2 spaces
29. Up 1 space
30. Left 1 space
31. Up 1 space
32. Right 1 space
33. Down 2 spaces (return over your line)
34. Right 2 spaces
35. Up 1 space
36. Left 1 space
37. Up 2 spaces
38. Right 1 space
39. Up 1 space

Add: eyes, mouth, whiskers

Dandy Duckling

Paper: one-inch grid

Starting point:

1. Place your paper vertically.
2. Find the top of the vertical line closest to the upper right corner of your paper.
3. Count down five full spaces.
4. Make a pencil dot on the intersection of the horizontal and vertical lines.
5. Put your pencil on the dot.

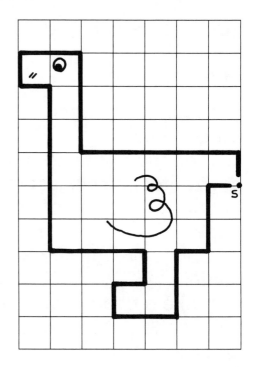

Move your pencil:

1. Left 1 space
2. Down 2 spaces
3. Left 1 space
4. Down 2 spaces
5. Left 2 spaces
6. Up 1 space
7. Right 1 space
8. Up 1 space
9. Left 3 spaces
10. Up 5 spaces
11. Left 1 space
12. Up 1 space
13. Right 2 spaces
14. Down 3 spaces
15. Right 5 spaces
16. Down 1 space

Add: eye, nostril, wing

Grid and Bear It, ©1987

Catch That Jogger

Paper: one-inch grid

Starting point:

1. Place your paper horizontally.
2. Find the right end of the horizontal line closest to the upper right corner of your paper.
3. Count five full spaces to the left.
4. Make a pencil dot on the intersection of the horizontal and vertical lines.
5. Put your pencil on the dot.

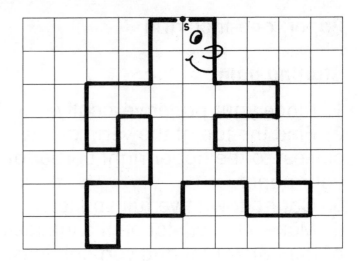

Move your pencil:

1. Right 1 space
2. Down 2 spaces
3. Right 2 spaces
4. Down 1 space
5. Left 2 spaces
6. Down 1 space
7. Right 2 spaces
8. Down 1 space
9. Right 1 space
10. Down 1 space
11. Left 2 spaces
12. Up 1 space
13. Left 2 spaces
14. Down 1 space
15. Left 2 spaces
16. Down 1 space
17. Left 1 space
18. Up 2 spaces
19. Right 2 spaces
20. Up 2 spaces
21. Left 1 space
22. Down 1 space
23. Left 1 space
24. Up 2 spaces
25. Right 2 spaces
26. Up 2 spaces
27. Right 1 space

Add: eye, mouth, nose

Rhonda Robot

Paper: one-inch grid

Starting point:

1. Place your paper horizontally.
2. Find the right end of the horizontal line closest to the upper right corner of your paper.
3. Count five full spaces to the left.
4. Make a pencil dot on the intersection of the horizontal and vertical lines.
5. Put your pencil on the dot.

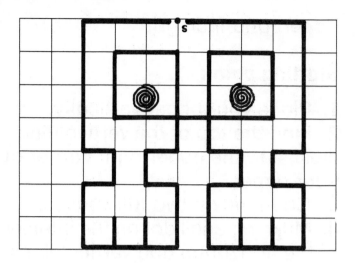

Move your pencil:

1. Right 4 spaces
2. Down 4 spaces
3. Left 1 space
4. Down 1 space
5. Right 1 space
6. Down 2 spaces
7. Left 1 space
8. Up 1 space
9. Down 1 space
(return over your line)
10. Left 1 space
11. Up 1 space
12. Down 1 space
(return over your line)
13. Left 1 space

14. Up 2 spaces
15. Right 1 space
16. Up 1 space
17. Left 1 space
18. Up 3 spaces
19. Right 2 spaces
20. Down 2 spaces
21. Left 5 spaces
22. Up 2 spaces
23. Right 2 spaces
24. Down 3 spaces
25. Left 1 space
26. Down 1 space
27. Right 1 space
28. Down 2 spaces

29. Left 1 space
30. Up 1 space
31. Down 1 space
(return over your line)
32. Left 1 space
33. Up 1 space
34. Down 1 space
(return over your line)
35. Left 1 space
36. Up 2 spaces
37. Right 1 space
38. Up 1 space
39. Left 1 space
40. Up 4 spaces
41. Right 3 spaces

Add: eyes

Weary Weight Lifter

Paper: one-inch grid

Starting point:

I. Place your paper vertically.
2. Find the top of the vertical line closest to the upper right corner of your paper.
3. Count down two full spaces.
4. Make a pencil dot on the intersection of the horizontal and vertical lines.
5. Put your pencil on the dot.

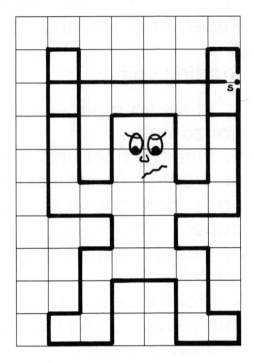

Move your pencil:

I. Down I space
2. Left I space
3. Right I space
(return over your line)
4. Down 3 spaces
5. Left 2 spaces
6. Down I space
7. Right I space
8. Down 2 spaces
9. Right I space
10. Down I space
11. Left 2 spaces
12. Up 2 spaces

13. Left 2 spaces
14. Down 2 spaces
15. Left 2 spaces
16. Up I space
17. Right I space
18. Up 2 spaces
19. Right I space
20. Up I space
21. Left 2 spaces
22. Up 3 spaces
23. Right I space
24. Left I space
(return over your line)

25. Up I space
26. Right 6 spaces
27. Up I space
28. Left I space
29. Down 4 spaces
30. Left I space
31. Up 2 spaces
32. Left 2 spaces
33. Down 2 spaces
34. Left I space
35. Up 4 spaces
36. Left I space
37. Down I space

Add: eyes, mouth, nose

Whose Teddy Bear?

Paper: one-inch grid

Starting point:

1. Place your paper vertically.
2. Find the top of the vertical line closest to the upper right corner of your paper.
3. Count down five full spaces.
4. Move left one full space.
5. Make a pencil dot on the intersection of the horizontal and vertical lines.
6. Put your pencil on the dot.

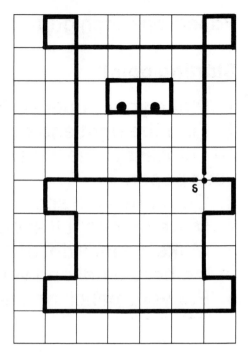

Move your pencil:

1. Left 2 spaces	10. Up 5 spaces	20. Down 2 spaces
2. Up 3 spaces	11. Left 1 space	21. Right 1 space
3. Right 1 space	12. Down 1 space	22. Down 1 space
4. Down 1 space	13. Right 6 spaces	23. Left 6 spaces
5. Left 2 spaces	14. Up 1 space	24. Up 1 space
6. Up 1 space	15. Left 1 space	25. Right 1 space
7. Right 1 space	16. Down 5 spaces	26. Up 2 spaces
8. Down 3 spaces	17. Right 1 space	27. Left 1 space
(return over your line)	18. Down 1 space	28. Up 1 space
9. Left 2 spaces	19. Left 1 space	29. Right 1 space

Add: eyes

Grid and Bear It, ©1987

Clever Kitty

Paper: one-inch grid

Starting point:

1. Place your paper vertically.
2. Find the right end of the horizontal line closest to the lower right corner of your paper.
3. Count two full spaces to the left.
4. Move up one full space.
5. Make a pencil dot on the intersection of the horizontal and vertical lines.
6. Put your pencil on the dot.

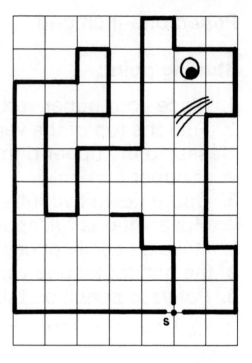

Move your pencil:

1. Right 2 spaces
2. Up 2 spaces
3. Left 1 space
4. Up 4 spaces
5. Right 1 space
6. Up 2 spaces
7. Left 2 spaces
8. Up 1 space
9. Left 1 space
10. Down 4 spaces
11. Left 2 spaces
12. Down 2 spaces
13. Left 1 space
14. Up 3 spaces
15. Right 2 spaces
16. Up 2 spaces
17. Left 1 space
18. Down 1 space
19. Left 2 spaces
20. Down 7 spaces
21. Right 5 spaces
22. Up 2 spaces
23. Left 1 space
24. Up 1 space
25. Left 1 space

Add: eye, whiskers

Grid and Bear It, ©1987

Lunch Table and Chairs

Paper: one-inch grid

Starting point:

1. Place your paper horizontally.
2. Find the left end of the horizontal line closest to the lower left corner of your paper.
3. Count three full spaces to the right.
4. Make a pencil dot on the intersection of the horizontal and vertical lines.
5. Put your pencil on the dot.

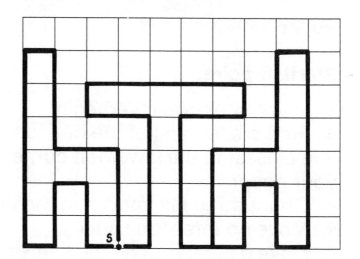

Move your pencil:

1. Left 1 space
2. Up 2 spaces
3. Left 1 space
4. Down 2 spaces
5. Left 1 space
6. Up 6 spaces
7. Right 1 space
8. Down 3 spaces
9. Right 2 spaces
10. Down 3 spaces

11. Right 1 space
12. Up 4 spaces
13. Left 2 spaces
14. Up 1 space
15. Right 5 spaces
16. Down 1 space
17. Left 2 spaces
18. Down 4 spaces
19. Right 1 space
20. Up 3 spaces

21. Right 2 spaces
22. Up 3 spaces
23. Right 1 space
24. Down 6 spaces
25. Left 1 space
26. Up 2 spaces
27. Left 1 space
28. Down 2 spaces
29. Left 1 space

As Fresh As a Flower

Paper: one-inch grid

Starting point:

1. Place your paper vertically.
2. Find the left end of the horizontal line closest to the lower left corner of your paper.
3. Count three full spaces to the right.
4. Move up three full spaces.
5. Make a pencil dot on the intersection of the horizontal and vertical lines.
6. Put your pencil on the dot.

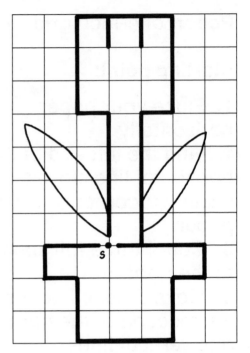

Move your pencil:

1. Left 2 spaces
2. Down 1 space
3. Right 1 space
4. Down 2 spaces
5. Right 3 spaces
6. Up 2 spaces
7. Right 1 space
8. Up 1 space
9. Left 2 spaces
10. Up 4 spaces
11. Right 1 space
12. Up 3 spaces
13. Left 1 space

14. Down 1 space
15. Up 1 space
(return over your line)
16. Left 1 space
17. Down 1 space
18. Up 1 space
(return over your line)
19. Left 1 space
20. Down 3 spaces
21. Right 1 space
22. Down 4 spaces
23. Right 1 space

Add: leaves

Sassy Snake

Paper: one-inch grid

Starting point:

1. Place your paper vertically.
2. Find the top of the vertical line closest to the upper left corner of your paper.
3. Count down five full spaces.
4. Move three full spaces to the right.
5. Make a pencil dot on the intersection of the horizontal and vertical lines.
6. Put your pencil on the dot.

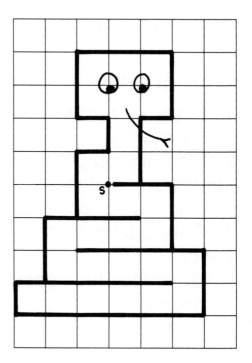

Move your pencil:

1. Right 1 space
2. Up 2 spaces
3. Right 1 space
4. Up 2 spaces
5. Left 3 spaces
6. Down 2 spaces
7. Right 1 space
8. Down 1 space
9. Left 1 space
10. Down 2 spaces
11. Right 2 spaces
12. Left 3 spaces
(return over your line)

13. Down 2 spaces
14. Right 4 spaces
15. Left 5 spaces
(return over your line)
16. Down 1 space
17. Right 6 spaces
18. Up 2 spaces
19. Left 4 spaces
20. Right 3 spaces
(return over your line)
21. Up 2 spaces
22. Left 1 space

Add: eyes, tongue

Grid and Bear It, ©1987

Harry Hippopotamus

Paper: one-inch grid

Starting point:

1. Place your paper horizontally.
2. Find the top of the vertical line closest to the upper left corner of your paper.
3. Count down three full spaces.
4. Move four full spaces to the right.
5. Make a pencil dot on the intersection of the horizontal and vertical lines.
6. Put your pencil on the dot.

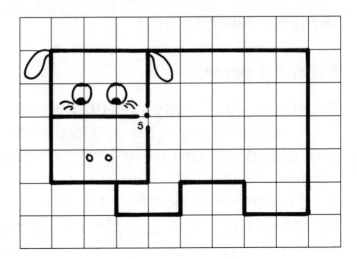

Move your pencil:

1. Left 3 spaces
2. Down 2 spaces
3. Right 3 spaces
4. Up 4 spaces
5. Right 5 spaces
6. Down 5 spaces
7. Left 2 spaces
8. Up 1 space
9. Left 2 spaces
10. Down 1 space
11. Left 2 spaces
12. Up 1 space
13. Left 2 spaces
(return over your line)
14. Up 4 spaces
(return over your line)
15. Right 3 spaces

Add: ears, eyes, nostrils

Monkey Business

Paper: one-inch grid

Starting point:

1. Place your paper horizontally.
2. Find the top of the vertical line closest to the upper right corner of your paper.
3. Count down four full spaces.
4. Move two full spaces to the left.
5. Make a pencil dot on the intersection of the horizontal and vertical lines.
6. Put your pencil on the dot.

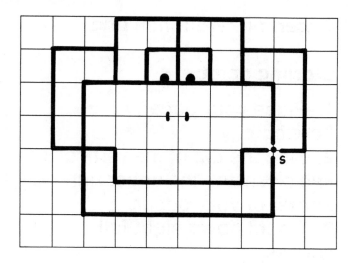

Move your pencil:

1. Down 2 spaces
2. Left 6 spaces
3. Up 2 spaces
4. Left 1 space
5. Up 3 spaces
6. Right 2 spaces
7. Up 1 space
8. Right 2 spaces
9. Down 1 space
10. Up 1 space
(return over your line)
11. Right 2 spaces
12. Down 2 spaces
13. Right 1 space

14. Down 2 spaces
15. Left 1 space
16. Down 1 space
17. Left 4 spaces
18. Up 1 space
19. Left 1 space
20. Up 2 spaces
21. Right 1 space
22. Up 1 space
23. Down 1 space
(return over your line)
24. Right 2 spaces
25. Up 1 space
26. Left 1 space

27. Down 1 space
28. Right 2 spaces
(return over your line)
29. Up 1 space
30. Left 1 space
31. Down 1 space
(return over your line)
32. Right 2 spaces
(return over your line)
33. Up 1 space
(return over your line)
34. Right 2 spaces
35. Down 3 spaces
36. Left 1 space

Add: eyes, nostrils

Henrietta Horse

Paper: one-half-inch grid

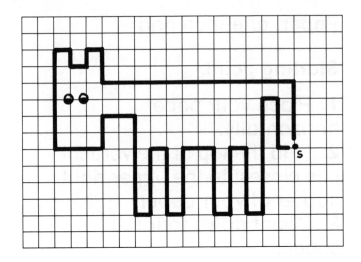

Starting point:

1. Place your paper horizontally.
2. Find the top of the vertical line closest to the upper right corner of your paper.
3. Count down eight full spaces.
4. Move three full spaces to the left.
5. Make a pencil dot on the intersection of the horizontal and vertical lines.
6. Put your pencil on the dot.

Move your pencil:

1. Left 1 space
2. Up 3 spaces
3. Left 1 space
4. Down 7 spaces
5. Left 1 space
6. Up 4 spaces
7. Left 1 space
8. Down 4 spaces
9. Left 1 space
10. Up 4 spaces
11. Left 2 spaces
12. Down 4 spaces
13. Left 1 space
14. Up 4 spaces
15. Left 1 space
16. Down 4 spaces
17. Left 1 space
18. Up 6 spaces
19. Left 2 spaces
20. Down 2 spaces
21. Left 3 spaces
22. Up 6 spaces
23. Right 1 space
24. Down 1 space
25. Right 1 space
26. Up 1 space
27. Right 1 space
28. Down 2 spaces
29. Right 12 spaces
30. Down 4 spaces

Add: eyes

Grid and Bear It, ©1987

Too-Late Turtle

Paper: one-half-inch grid

Starting point:

1. Place your paper horizontally.
2. Find the top of the vertical line closest to the upper right corner of your paper.
3. Count down seven full spaces.
4. Move five full spaces to the left.
5. Make a pencil dot on the intersection of the horizontal and vertical lines.
6. Put your pencil on the dot.

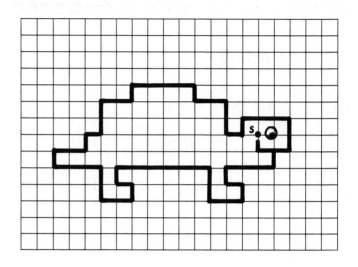

Move your pencil:

1. Down 1 space
2. Right 2 spaces
3. Up 2 spaces
4. Left 3 spaces
5. Down 1 space
6. Left 1 space
7. Up 2 spaces
8. Left 2 spaces
9. Up 1 space
10. Left 4 spaces
11. Down 1 space

12. Left 2 spaces
13. Down 2 spaces
14. Left 1 space
15. Down 1 space
16. Left 2 spaces
17. Down 1 space
18. Right 3 spaces
19. Down 2 spaces
20. Right 2 spaces
21. Up 1 space
22. Left 1 space

23. Up 1 space
24. Right 6 spaces
25. Down 2 spaces
26. Right 2 spaces
27. Up 1 space
28. Left 1 space
29. Up 1 space
30. Right 3 spaces
31. Up 1 space

Add: eye

Henrietta Horse

Paper: one-half-inch coordinate grid

Starting point: P–5

Move your pencil to:

O–5	M–5	I–5	G–1	A–5	C–11
O–8	L–5	I–1	F–1	A–11	D–11
N–8	L–1	H–1	F–7	B–11	D–9
N–1	K–1	H–5	D–7	B–10	P–9
M–1	K–5	G–5	D–5	C–10	P–5

Add: eyes

- -

Too-Late Turtle

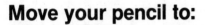

Paper: one-half-inch coordinate grid

Starting point: O–8

Move your pencil to:

O–7	M–10	E–8	E–4	L–4	P–7
Q–7	K–10	D–8	G–4	N–4	
Q–9	K–11	D–7	G–5	N–5	
N–9	G–11	B–7	F–5	M–5	
N–8	G–10	B–6	F–6	M–6	
M–8	E–10	E–6	L–6	P–6	

Add: eye

Baby Oscar Ostrich

Paper: one-half-inch grid

Starting point:

1. Place your paper vertically.
2. Find the left end of the horizontal line closest to the lower left corner of your paper.
3. Count seven full spaces to the right.
4. Move up one full space.
5. Make a pencil dot on the intersection of the horizontal and vertical lines.
6. Put your pencil on the dot.

Move your pencil:

1. Up 6 spaces
2. Left 1 space
3. Up 2 spaces
4. Left 4 spaces
5. Up 3 spaces
6. Left 1 space
7. Up 1 space
8. Right 2 spaces
9. Down 3 spaces
10. Right 2 spaces
11. Up 1 space
12. Left 1 space
13. Up 5 spaces
14. Right 1 space
15. Up 1 space
16. Right 1 space
17. Down 2 spaces
18. Left 1 space
19. Down 3 spaces
20. Right 1 space
21. Up 2 spaces
22. Right 2 spaces
23. Down 1 space
24. Left 1 space
25. Down 2 spaces
26. Right 2 spaces
27. Up 8 spaces
28. Right 2 spaces
29. Down 2 spaces
30. Right 2 spaces
31. Down 1 space
32. Left 3 spaces
33. Down 9 spaces
34. Left 2 spaces
35. Down 5 spaces
36. Right 2 spaces
37. Down 1 space
38. Left 3 spaces

Add: eye

Grid and Bear It, ©1987

Miss Bunny T. Rabbit

Paper: one-half-inch grid

Starting point:

1. Place your paper vertically.
2. Find the right end of the horizontal line closest to the lower right corner of your paper.
3. Count one full space to the left.
4. Move up one full space.
5. Make a pencil dot on the intersection of the horizontal and vertical lines.
6. Put your pencil on the dot.

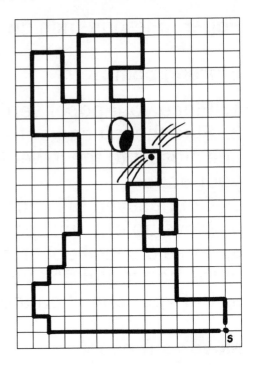

Move your pencil:

1. Left 11 spaces
2. Up 1 space
3. Left 1 space
4. Up 2 spaces
5. Right 1 space
6. Up 1 space
7. Right 1 space
8. Up 2 spaces
9. Right 1 space
10. Up 6 spaces
11. Left 3 spaces
12. Up 5 spaces

13. Right 2 spaces
14. Down 3 spaces
15. Right 1 space
16. Up 4 spaces
17. Right 4 spaces
18. Down 2 spaces
19. Left 2 spaces
20. Down 2 spaces
21. Right 2 spaces
22. Down 3 spaces
23. Right 1 space
24. Down 2 spaces

25. Left 2 spaces
26. Down 1 space
27. Right 3 spaces
28. Down 2 spaces
29. Left 1 space
30. Up 1 space
31. Left 1 space
32. Down 2 spaces
33. Right 2 spaces
34. Down 3 spaces
35. Right 3 spaces
36. Down 2 spaces

Add: eye, nose, whiskers

Baby Oscar Ostrich

Paper: one-half-inch coordinate grid

Starting point: A–7

Move your pencil to:

G–7	M–11	Q–9	N–6	Q–3	B–4
G–8	J–11	Q–8	M–6	Q–1	A–4
I–8	J–9	O–8	M–7	P–1	A–7
I–12	K–9	O–9	K–7	P–4	
L–12	K–10	L–9	K–5	G–4	
L–13	P–10	L–8	S–5	G–6	
M–13	P–9	N–8	S–3	B–6	

Turn your paper and add: eye

- -

Miss Bunny T. Rabbit

Paper: one-half-inch coordinate grid

Starting point: A–1

Move your pencil to:

A–12	E–11	R–11	Q–8	J–7	H–6
B–12	G–11	O–11	O–8	I–7	F–6
B–13	G–10	O–10	O–6	I–4	F–4
D–13	M–10	S–10	L–6	G–4	C–4
D–12	M–13	S–6	L–5	G–5	C–1
E–12	R–13	Q–6	J–5	H–5	A–1

Turn your paper and add: eye, nose, whiskers

Can You Bear It?

Paper: one-half-inch grid

Starting point:

1. Place your paper horizontally.
2. Find the left end of the horizontal line closest to the upper left corner of your paper.
3. Count five full spaces to the right.
4. Move down six full spaces.
5. Make a pencil dot on the intersection of the horizontal and vertical lines.
6. Put your pencil on the dot.

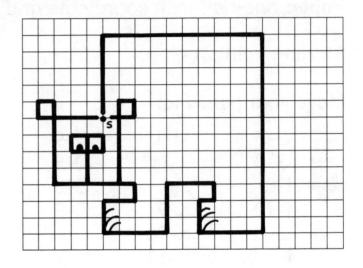

Move your pencil:

1. Right 2 spaces
2. Up 1 space
3. Left 1 space
4. Down 5 spaces
5. Left 2 spaces
6. Up 3 spaces
7. Right 1 space
8. Down 1 space
9. Left 2 spaces
10. Up 1 space
11. Right 1 space
12. Down 3 spaces (return over your line)
13. Left 2 spaces
14. Up 5 spaces
15. Left 1 space
16. Down 1 space
17. Right 4 spaces
18. Up 5 spaces
19. Right 10 spaces
20. Down 12 spaces
21. Left 4 spaces
22. Up 2 spaces
23. Right 1 space
24. Up 1 space
25. Left 3 spaces
26. Down 3 spaces
27. Left 4 spaces
28. Up 2 spaces
29. Right 2 spaces
30. Up 1 space
31. Left 1 space

Add: claws, eyes

Grid and Bear It, ©1987

Sally

Paper: one-half-inch grid

Starting point:
1. Place your paper vertically.
2. Find the left end of the horizontal line closest to the upper left corner of your paper.
3. Count seven full spaces to the right.
4. Move down two full spaces.
5. Make a pencil dot on the intersection of the horizontal and vertical lines.
6. Put your pencil on the dot.

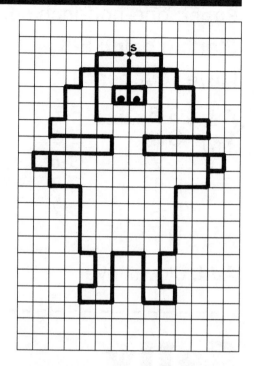

Move your pencil:

1. Down 3 spaces
2. Right 1 space
3. Up 1 space
4. Left 2 spaces
5. Down 1 space
6. Right 1 space
7. Up 3 spaces
(return over your line)
8. Right 2 spaces
9. Down 1 space
10. Right 1 space
11. Down 1 space
12. Right 1 space
13. Down 2 spaces
14. Right 1 space
15. Down 1 space
16. Left 4 spaces
17. Down 1 space
18. Right 4 spaces
19. Down 1 space
20. Right 1 space

21. Up 1 space
22. Left 1 space
23. Down 2 spaces
(return over your line)
24. Left 2 spaces
25. Down 4 spaces
26. Left 1 space
27. Down 2 spaces
28. Right 1 space
29. Down 1 space
30. Left 2 spaces
31. Up 3 spaces
32. Left 2 spaces
33. Down 3 spaces
34. Left 2 spaces
35. Up 1 space
36. Right 1 space
37. Up 2 spaces
38. Left 1 space
39. Up 4 spaces
40. Left 2 spaces

41. Up 2 spaces
42. Left 1 space
43. Down 1 space
44. Right 1 space
45. Up 1 space
(return over your line)
46. Right 4 spaces
47. Up 1 space
48. Left 4 spaces
49. Up 1 space
50. Right 1 space
51. Up 2 spaces
52. Right 1 space
53. Up 1 space
54. Right 5 spaces
55. Down 3 spaces
56. Left 4 spaces
57. Up 4 spaces
58. Right 2 spaces

Add: eyes

Can You Bear It?

Paper: one-half-inch coordinate grid

Starting point: E-8

Move your pencil to:

G-8	E-7	Return over	A-8	K-3	E-3
G-9	E-6	your line to	E-8	L-3	G-3
F-9	C-6	D-4	E-13	L-4	G-4
F-4	C-7	B-4	O-13	I-4	F-4
D-4	D-7	B-9	O-1	I-1	
D-7		A-9	K-1	E-1	

Add: claws, eyes

- -

Sally

Paper: one-half-inch coordinate grid

Starting point: B-7

Move your pencil to:

E-7	C-9	G-12	N-10	N-5	G-6
E-8	C-7	G-8	N-9	N-4	G-2
D-8	Return over	H-8	P-9	J-4	F-2
D-6	your line to	H-12	P-10	J-2	F-3
E-6	B-7	I-12	Q-10	H-2	D-3
E-7	B-9	I-13	Q-8	H-1	D-4
Return over	C-9	H-13	N-8	I-1	C-4
your line to	C-10	H-12	N-6	I-2	C-5
C-7	D-10	Return over	Q-6	Return over	B-5
C-5	D-11	your line to	Q-4	your line to	B-7
F-5	F-11	J-12	P-4	H-2	
F-9	F-12	J-10	P-5	H-6	

Turn your paper and add: eyes

Slowpoke Snail

Paper: one-half-inch grid

Starting point:

1. Place your paper horizontally.
2. Find the left end of the horizontal line closest to the upper left corner of your paper.
3. Count ten full spaces to the right.
4. Move down seven full spaces.
5. Make a pencil dot on the intersection of the horizontal and vertical lines.
6. Put your pencil on the dot.

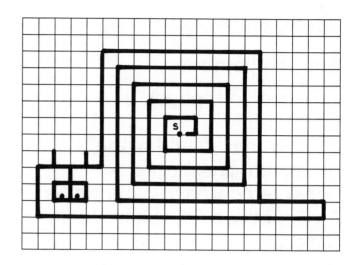

Move your pencil:

1. Right 1 space
2. Up 1 space
3. Left 2 spaces
4. Down 2 spaces
5. Right 3 spaces
6. Up 3 spaces
7. Left 4 spaces
8. Down 4 spaces
9. Right 5 spaces
10. Up 5 spaces
11. Left 6 spaces
12. Down 6 spaces
13. Right 7 spaces
14. Up 7 spaces

15. Left 8 spaces
16. Down 8 spaces
17. Right 9 spaces
18. Up 9 spaces
19. Left 10 spaces
20. Down 7 spaces
21. Left 1 space
22. Up 1 space
23. Down 1 space
(return over your line)
24. Left 1 space
25. Down 2 spaces
26. Right 1 space
27. Up 1 space

28. Left 2 spaces
29. Down 1 space
30. Right 1 space
31. Up 2 spaces
(return over your line)
32. Left 1 space
33. Up 1 space
34. Down 1 space
(return over your line)
35. Left 1 space
36. Down 3 spaces
37. Right 18 spaces
38. Up 1 space
39. Left 4 spaces

Add: eyes

Energetic Engine

Paper: one-half-inch grid

Starting point:

1. Place your paper horizontally.
2. Find the left end of the horizontal line closest to the upper left corner of your paper.
3. Count two full spaces to the right.
4. Move down six full spaces.
5. Make a pencil dot on the intersection of the horizontal and vertical lines.
6. Put your pencil on the dot.

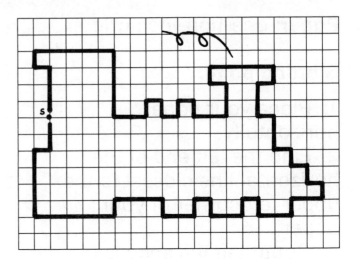

Move your pencil:

1. Up 3 spaces	17. Up 1 space	33. Up 1 space
2. Left 1 space	18. Right 4 spaces	34. Left 1 space
3. Up 1 space	19. Down 1 space	35. Down 1 space
4. Right 5 spaces	20. Left 1 space	36. Left 2 spaces
5. Down 4 spaces	21. Down 2 spaces	37. Up 1 space
6. Right 2 spaces	22. Right 1 space	38. Left 1 space
7. Up 1 space	23. Down 2 spaces	39. Down 1 space
8. Right 1 space	24. Right 1 space	40. Left 2 spaces
9. Down 1 space	25. Down 1 space	41. Up 1 space
10. Right 1 space	26. Right 1 space	42. Left 3 spaces
11. Up 1 space	27. Down 1 space	43. Down 1 space
12. Right 1 space	28. Right 1 space	44. Left 5 spaces
13. Down 1 space	29. Down 1 space	45. Up 4 spaces
14. Right 2 spaces	30. Left 2 spaces	46. Right 1 space
15. Up 2 spaces	31. Down 1 space	47. Up 2 spaces
16. Left 1 space	32. Left 2 spaces	

Add: smoke

Slowpoke Snail

Paper: one-half-inch coordinate gird

Starting point: J–8

Move your pencil to:

K–8	M–6	F–4	Return over	B–4	Return over
K–9	M–11	O–4	your line to	C–4	your line to
I–9	G–11	O–13	D–6	Return over	B–6
I–7	G–5	E–13	C–6	your line to	A–6
L–7	N–5	E–6	C–4	C–6	A–3
L–10	N–12	D–6	D–4	B–6	S–3
H–10	F–12	D–7	D–5	B–7	S–4
H–6			B–5		O–4

Add: eyes

- -

Energetic Engine

Paper: one-half-inch coordinate grid

Starting point: B–8

Move your pencil to:

B–11	I–8	L–11	Q–5	O–3	I–3
A–11	J–8	P–11	R–5	N–3	F–3
A–12	J–9	P–10	R–4	N–2	F–2
F–12	K–9	O–10	S–4	L–2	A–2
F–8	K–8	O–8	S–3	L–3	A–6
H–8	M–8	P–8	Q–3	K–3	B–6
H–9	M–10	P–6	Q–2	K–2	B–8
I–9	L–10	Q–6	O–2	I–2	

Add: smoke

Bozo's Boxcar

Paper: one-half-inch grid

Starting point:

1. Place your paper horizontally.
2. Find the left end of the horizontal line closest to the lower left corner of your paper.
3. Count twelve full spaces to the right.
4. Move up two full spaces.
5. Make a pencil dot on the intersection of the horizontal and vertical lines.
6. Put your pencil on the dot.

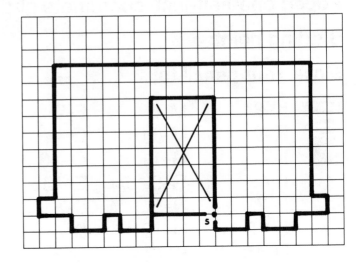

Move your pencil:

1. Left 4 spaces
2. Up 7 spaces
3. Right 4 spaces
4. Down 8 spaces
5. Right 2 spaces
6. Up 1 space
7. Right 1 space
8. Down 1 space
9. Right 2 spaces
10. Up 1 space
11. Right 2 spaces
12. Up 1 space
13. Left 1 space
14. Up 8 spaces
15. Left 16 spaces
16. Down 8 spaces
17. Left 1 space
18. Down 1 space
19. Right 2 spaces
20. Down 1 space
21. Right 2 spaces
22. Up 1 space
23. Right 1 space
24. Down 1 space
25. Right 2 spaces
26. Up 1 space

Add: a big X on the door

Ferdi's Flatcar

Paper: one-half-inch grid

Starting point:

1. Place your paper horizontally.
2. Find the left end of the horizontal line closest to the lower left corner of your paper.
3. Count one full space to the right.
4. Move up three full spaces.
5. Make a pencil dot on the intersection of the horizontal and vertical lines.
6. Put your pencil on the dot.

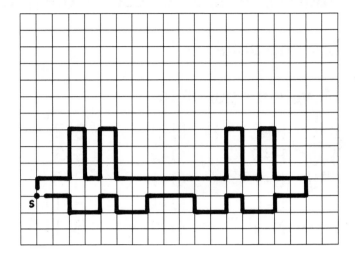

Move your pencil:

1. Up 1 space	**13.** Down 3 spaces	**25.** Down 1 space
2. Right 2 spaces	**14.** Right 1 space	**26.** Left 2 spaces
3. Up 3 spaces	**15.** Up 3 spaces	**27.** Up 1 space
4. Right 1 space	**16.** Right 1 space	**28.** Left 3 spaces
5. Down 3 spaces	**17.** Down 3 spaces	**29.** Down 1 space
6. Right 1 space	**18.** Right 2 spaces	**30.** Left 2 spaces
7. Up 3 spaces	**19.** Down 1 space	**31.** Up 1 space
8. Right 1 space	**20.** Left 2 spaces	**32.** Left 1 space
9. Down 3 spaces	**21.** Down 1 space	**33.** Down 1 space
10. Right 7 spaces	**22.** Left 2 spaces	**34.** Left 2 spaces
11. Up 3 spaces	**23.** Up 1 space	**35.** Up 1 space
12. Right 1 space	**24.** Left 1 space	**36.** Left 2 spaces

Bozo's Boxcar

Paper: one-half-inch coordinate grid

Starting point: L–2

Move your pencil to:

H–2	N–2	S–2	B–3	E–1	H–2
H–9	O–2	S–3	A–3	E–2
L–9	O–1	R–3	A–2	F–2
L–1	Q–1	R–11	C–2	F–1
N–1	Q–2	B–11	C–1	H–1

Add: a big X on the door

- -

Ferdi's Flatcar

Paper: one-half-inch coordinate grid

Starting point: A–2

Move your pencil to:

A–3	E–6	N–3	R–2	M–1	F–2
C–3	F–6	O–3	P–2	K–1	E–2
C–6	F–3	O–6	P–1	K–2	E–1
D–6	M–3	P–6	N–1	H–2	C–1
D–3	M–6	P–3	N–2	H–1	C–2
E–3	N–6	R–3	M–2	F–1	A–2

Grid and Bear It, ©1987

Train Tanker Car

Paper: one-half-inch grid

Starting point:

1. Place your paper horizontally.
2. Find the left end of the horizontal line closest to the lower left corner of your paper.
3. Count one full space to the right.
4. Move up two full spaces.
5. Make a pencil dot on the intersection of the horizontal and vertical lines.
6. Put your pencil on the dot.

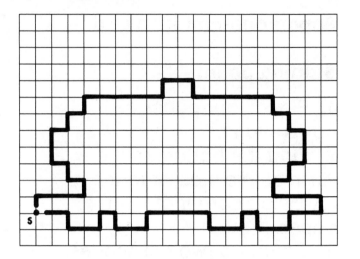

Move your pencil:

1. Up 1 space
2. Right 3 spaces
3. Up 1 space
4. Left 1 space
5. Up 1 space
6. Left 1 space
7. Up 2 spaces
8. Right 1 space
9. Up 1 space
10. Right 1 space
11. Up 1 space
12. Right 5 spaces
13. Up 1 space
14. Right 2 spaces
15. Down 1 space
16. Right 5 spaces
17. Down 1 space
18. Right 1 space
19. Down 1 space
20. Right 1 space
21. Down 2 spaces
22. Left 1 space
23. Down 1 space
24. Left 1 space
25. Down 1 space
26. Right 3 spaces
27. Down 1 space
28. Left 2 spaces
29. Down 1 space
30. Left 2 spaces
31. Up 1 space
32. Left 1 space
33. Down 1 space
34. Left 2 spaces
35. Up 1 space
36. Left 4 spaces
37. Down 1 space
38. Left 2 spaces
39. Up 1 space
40. Left 1 space
41. Down 1 space
42. Left 2 spaces
43. Up 1 space
44. Left 2 spaces

Completer Caboose

Paper: one-half-inch grid

Starting point:

1. Place your paper horizontally.
2. Find the bottom of the vertical line closest to the lower left corner of your paper.
3. Count up two full spaces.
4. Move right one full space.
5. Make a pencil dot on the intersection of the horizontal and vertical lines.
6. Put your pencil on the dot.

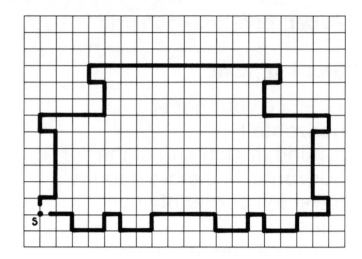

Move your pencil:

1. Up 1 space	13. Down 2 spaces	25. Down 1 space
2. Right 1 space	14. Right 4 spaces	26. Left 2 spaces
3. Up 4 spaces	15. Down 1 space	27. Up 1 space
4. Left 1 space	16. Left 1 space	28. Left 4 spaces
5. Up 1 space	17. Down 4 spaces	29. Down 1 space
6. Right 4 spaces	18. Right 1 space	30. Left 2 spaces
7. Up 2 spaces	19. Down 1 space	31. Up 1 space
8. Left 1 space	20. Left 2 spaces	32. Left 1 space
9. Up 1 space	21. Down 1 space	33. Down 1 space
10. Right 12 spaces	22. Left 2 spaces	34. Left 2 spaces
11. Down 1 space	23. Up 1 space	35. Up 1 space
12. Left 1 space	24. Left 1 space	36. Left 2 spaces

Train Tanker Car

Paper: one-half-inch coordinate grid

Starting point: A–2

Move your pencil to:

A–3	C–8	P–8	P–3	N–I	E–I
D–3	D–8	Q–8	S–3	L–I	C–I
D–4	D–9	Q–7	S–2	L–2	C–2
C–4	I–9	R–7	Q–2	H–2	A–2
C–5	I–10	R–5	Q–I	H–I	
B–5	K–10	Q–5	O–I	F–I	
B–7	K–9	Q–4	O–2	F–2	
C–7	P–9	P–4	N–2	E–2	

Completer Caboose

Paper: one-half-inch coordinate grid

Starting point: A–2

Move your pencil to:

A–3	E–10	O–8	S–2	N–I	F–2
B–3	D–10	S–8	Q–2	L–I	E–2
B–7	D–II	S–7	Q–I	L–2	E–I
A–7	P–II	R–7	O–I	H–2	C–I
A–8	P–10	R–3	O–2	H–I	C–2
E–8	O–10	S–3	N–2	F–I	A–2

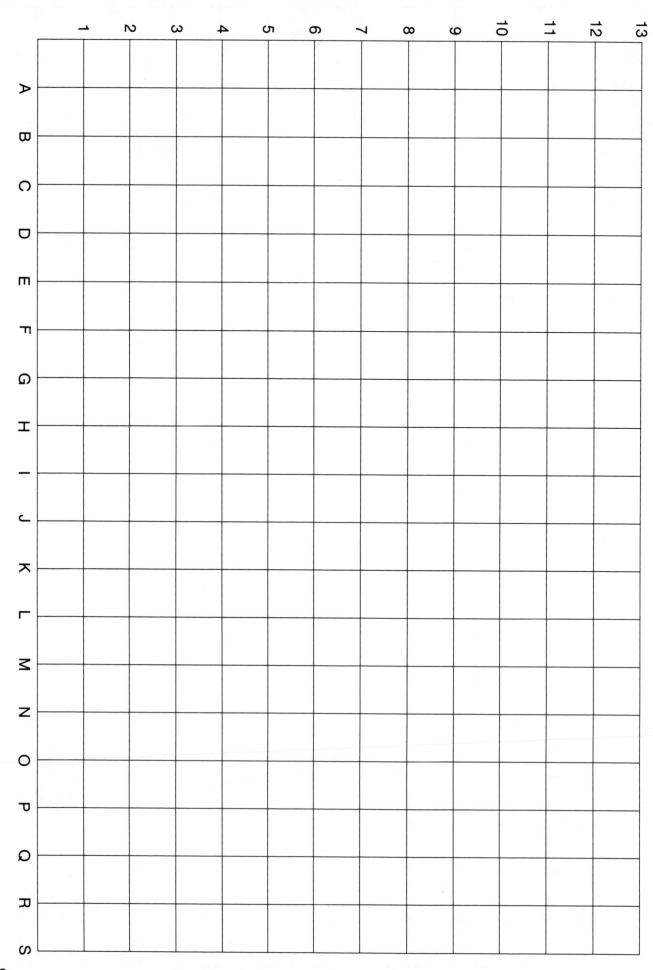